KORGI

CREATED BY

ANN & CHRISTIAN SLADE

top
Shelf
PRODUCTIONS

Korgi (Book 3): A Hollow Beginning © & tm 2011 Christian Slade.

Published by
Top Shelf Productions
PO Box 1282
Marietta, GA 30061-1282
USA

Publishers:
Chris Staros & Brett Warnock

Visit our online catalog at
www.topshelfcomix.com.

First Printing, August 2011. Printed in Canada.

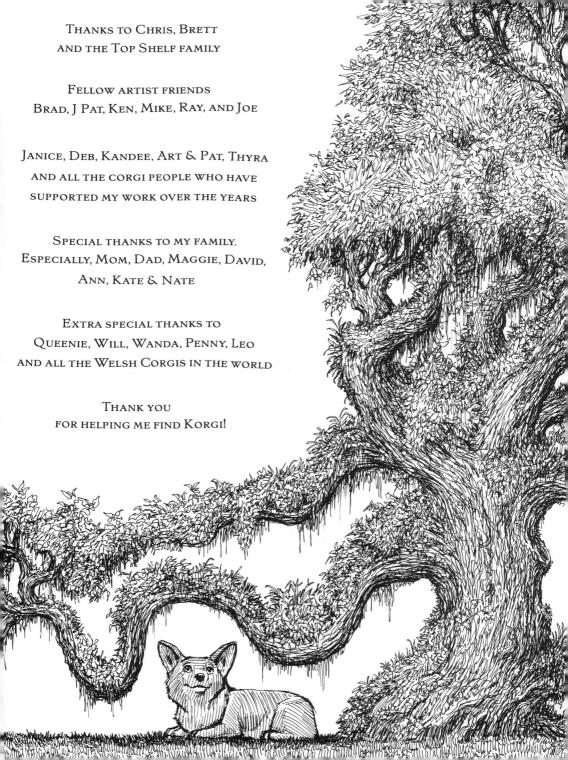

THANKS TO CHRIS, BRETT
AND THE TOP SHELF FAMILY

FELLOW ARTIST FRIENDS
BRAD, J PAT, KEN, MIKE, RAY, AND JOE

JANICE, DEB, KANDEE, ART & PAT, THYRA
AND ALL THE CORGI PEOPLE WHO HAVE
SUPPORTED MY WORK OVER THE YEARS

SPECIAL THANKS TO MY FAMILY.
ESPECIALLY, MOM, DAD, MAGGIE, DAVID,
ANN, KATE & NATE

EXTRA SPECIAL THANKS TO
QUEENIE, WILL, WANDA, PENNY, LEO
AND ALL THE WELSH CORGIS IN THE WORLD

THANK YOU
FOR HELPING ME FIND KORGI!

3

HELLO AGAIN, CURIOUS READER!
IT'S SO GOOD TO SEE YOU RETURN.

THE WORLD IS A WONDER. AND THE THINGS THAT LIE
WITHIN ARE EVEN MORE WONDROUS.

ONE OF THESE WONDERFUL THINGS THAT I OFTEN PONDER
IS HOW CREATURES AND PLACES BEGIN. THE LARGE GIANT OAK TREE
WAS ONCE A TINY ACORN NO BIGGER THAN A FLOWER. EACH CREATURE
LIVING IN, UNDER AND ABOVE THE FOREST HAS ITS OWN UNIQUE SPOT.
AS DIFFERENT AS WE ARE FROM EACH OTHER, WE ARE ALSO THE
SAME IN MANY WAYS. ONE OF THE THINGS THAT BINDS US IS
THAT WE ALL HAVE A BEGINNING. OVER THE MANY YEARS I HAVE
BEEN HERE, I HAVE MADE IT AN ADVENTURE TO DISCOVER HOW
THE MAGICAL WORLD AROUND ME BEGAN.

IN THIS SPECIAL BOOK, THE VERY BEGINNINGS OF KORGI
HOLLOW ITSELF WILL BE REVEALED. FOR IN THIS STORY YOU WILL FIND
ANOTHER TALE, AN OLDER TALE, TOLD BY NONE OTHER THAN MYSELF.

SO YOU'LL BE SEEING ME IN A SHORT BIT. IN THE
MEANTIME, DO FIND YOUR BEST READING
PLACE, CURL UP WITH YOUR FAVORITE BLANKET,
AND PREPARE YOURSELF FOR,

"A HOLLOW BEGINNING!"

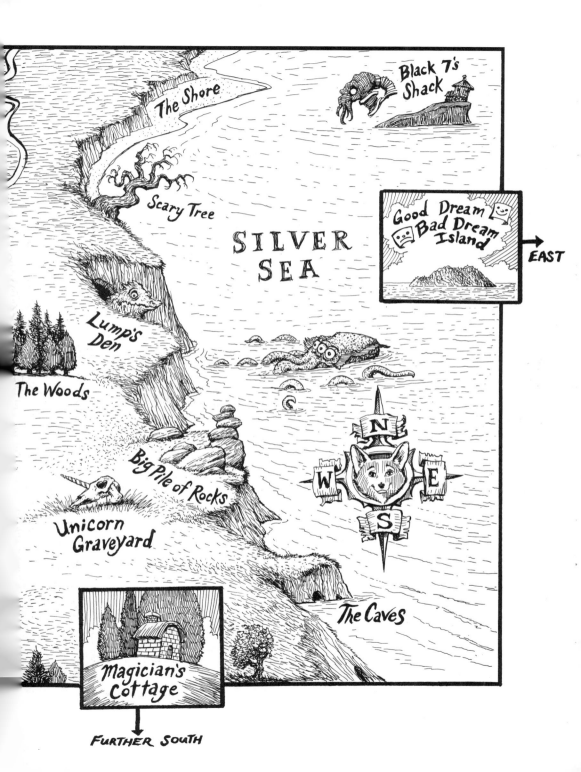

Black 7's
Shack

The Shore

Scary Tree

SILVER
SEA

Good Dream
Bad Dream
Island

EAST

Lump's
Den

The Woods

Big Pile of Rocks

N

W   E

S

Unicorn
Graveyard

The Caves

Magician's
Cottage

FURTHER SOUTH

CHARACTERS

IVY Sprout's best friend and caretaker. Ivy found Sprout when they were both very young. As with many Mollies, Ivy will grow up alongside her Korgi cub, who helps her realize her potential. Ivy spends a lot of time caring for Sprout, helping out in the Korgi community and using her flying ability to patrol the outer edges of surrounding lands.

SPROUT Ivy's Korgi cub and best friend. Even though Sprout is young, he possesses the great talent of fire breathing, a rare skill that has not been seen in a Korgi for many generations. Sprout is a curious cub who enjoys exploring the lands surrounding Korgi Hollow with Ivy. He also has a great passion for food!

WART Having lived in Korgi Hollow for a long time, Wart collects books and is the town's historian, scroll keeper, and librarian. He also counsels many of the Hollow's leaders, advising on important matters that concern the growth and safety of the village.

CREEPHOG Dirty, sti... and, well... creepy are a fe... of the words to describe these creatures. Creephog... like to dwell undergroun... or be partially buried in di... which they also like to ea... They are natural diggers, which makes them tough to spot. They are excellen... spies. That said, their small brains and constant... bickering get in the way o... retaining much informatio...

OTTO Living just outside the border of Korgi Hollow in the Burrow community, Otto practices his archery skills every day. He has a history of playing practical jokes with his good friends Ivy and Sprout.

SCARLETT
A FRIEND OF LUMP WHO ENJOYS SINGING. SHE IS OLDER THAN LUMP AND HELPED LOOK AFTER HIM AS HE GREW UP IN THE OCEANSIDE CAVE.

DEROG-GLAW
THIS TWO-HEADED MONSTER IS THE RESULT OF TWO EVIL PRINCES (ONE NAMED DEROG, THE OTHER NAMED GLAW) WHOSE CAULDRON WENT AWRY AND EXPLODED WHEN THEY WERE USING POTIONS THAT WOULD HELP REVEAL THEIR ESCAPED KORGI PRISONERS. WHEN THE MAGIC BACKFIRED, DEROG AND GLAW WERE FUSED TOGETHER INTO A HIDEOUS CREATURE BURIED IN THE DUNGEON BELOW THE COLLAPSED KINGDOM. OVER MANY, MANY YEARS, DEROG-GLAW HAVE USED THEIR MIND CONTROL OVER THE CREEPHOGS, WHO HAVE NO CHOICE BUT TO SERVE THEIR MASTER AND HELP IT RECOVER. THE ONLY WAY DEROG-GLAW CAN SPLIT AND BECOME TWO AGAIN IS BY DRINKING THE BLOOD OF A FIRE-BREATHING KORGI.

LUMP
A FRIEND TO ALL THE MOLLIES AND KORGIS, LUMP TRIES TO HELP THEM IN ANY WAY HE CAN. THIS IS SOMETIMES DIFFICULT, AS HE IS VERY CLUMSY AND EASILY SCARED. LUMP WAS ABANDONED WHEN HE WAS A YOUNG DRAGON BECAUSE HE CANNOT BREATHE FIRE AND DOESN'T HAVE WINGS. HE GREW UP LIVING IN A CAVE ALONG THE COAST OF THE SILVER SEA.

MOLLIES & KORGIS
MOLLIES USED TO BE A TINY, LAZY GROUP OF WOODLAND FOLK. THIS CHANGED WHEN THE CUTE AND FUZZY KORGIS CAME TO LIVE WITH THEM. SINCE THEN, THE MOLLIES, WHILE STILL SMALL, ARE FULL OF LIFE AND ENERGY. KORGIS ARE FUZZY ANIMALS WITH BIG EARS, BIG SMILES AND EVEN BIGGER HEARTS THAT HAVE THE SPECIAL ABILITY TO HELP THOSE AROUND THEM BY THEIR VERY PRESENCE. OFTEN, THOSE IN THE COMPANY OF KORGIS DISCOVER POWERS THEY DIDN'T KNOW THEY HAD, SUCH AS THE ABILITY TO FLY OR BUILD ELABORATE THINGS.

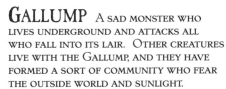

GALLUMP
A SAD MONSTER WHO LIVES UNDERGROUND AND ATTACKS ALL WHO FALL INTO ITS LAIR. OTHER CREATURES LIVE WITH THE GALLUMP, AND THEY HAVE FORMED A SORT OF COMMUNITY WHO FEAR THE OUTSIDE WORLD AND SUNLIGHT.

LIEUTENANT
A CREATURE WHO OFTEN KEEPS COMPANY WITH THE GALLUMP. HE GOT HIS SPACE OUTFIT BY LOOTING THE CRASHED ALIEN SHIP THAT LOOMS ABOVE THE GALLUMP'S LAIR.

KNICK & NACK
SMALL TWIN SNAILS WHO ARE OFTEN SEEN AROUND THE HOLLOW. THEY LIKE RACING EACH OTHER, ROWING BOATS ALONG THE CREEKS AND TELLING SCARY STORIES.

BLACK 7
A MAROONED ALIEN WHOSE SHIP CRASHED LONG AGO ON THE BORDERING LANDS OF KORGI HOLLOW.

BOTS
REMOTE-CONTROLLED TOYS BUILT AND COLLECTED BY BLACK 7.

Flashback Characters

Magician & Korgis

In a distant land long ago, the Magician lived in a cottage with a herd of magical Korgis. These seven Korgis would eventually be the first ones to live with Mollies and form the community that would become Korgi Hollow.

Auntie Pluther

Of the royal Pluther family bloodline. Auntie is a cruel woman who gives the Korgis to her twin prince nephews, Derog and Glaw, for their thirteenth birthday present.

KING AND QUEEN PLUTHER
A KIND ROYAL COUPLE. THEIR RULE IS PEACEFUL
AND THE KINGDOM HAS NEVER BEEN HAPPIER.

NICHOLAS
HEAD OF THE ROYAL PLUTHER GUARD.

VULCHANT
THIS UNSCRUPULOUS CHARACTER
SPENDS HIS DAYS PEDDLING TRAPPED
CREATURES AT THE MARKETPLACE IN
THE CITY OF MISER MOUNTAIN.

BANDITS

THESE VILE THIEVES TRAVEL DISTANT LANDS, STEALING AND TRAPPING RARE CREATURES TO SELL AT MARKET.

DEROG & GLAW

UNKNOWN TO THEIR PARENTS, DEROG AND GLAW ARE TWO EVIL PRINCES WHO ARE PLOTTING TO DESTROY THEIR PARENTS AND ENSLAVE THE PEOPLE. THEY OFTEN EXPERIMENT WITH THE DARKEST KINDS OF MAGIC AND USE THEIR POWERS FOR CRUEL AND SINISTER DEEDS.